Pat the pig's birthday
and other stories

Nelson

The sports day

"I have a sack," said Tom.
"I am in a race.
I am in the sack race."

"I have a big sack.
I will jump in my sack.
I will go fast."

"I am in a race.

I am in the sack race," said Jenny.

"I will jump in my sack."

It is time for the race.
Tom is in his sack.
Jenny is in her sack.

"One, two, three, go,"
said Tom's Dad.
"Jump as fast as you can."

Tom was in front.

He fell over.

Jenny went past.

Tom got up.

He went very fast.

8

"Hello, Tom," said his Dad.
"You have jumped fast but
you have jumped back
to the start."

Pat the pig's birthday

It is Pat the pig's birthday.
"I will have a party,"
said Pat.

"Don't forget to come
to my party," said Pat.
"We will not forget,"
said Meg and Ben.
"We will not forget,"
said Jip and Sam.

"It is my birthday,"
said Pat to Deb.
"Don't forget to come
to my party."

"I will put a knot
in my tail," said Deb.
"Then I will not forget."

Deb put a big knot
in her tail.
"I will not forget
the party now," said Deb.

Jip and Meg came
to the party.
Sam and Ben came
to the party.

Deb came to the party.
She had a knot in her tail.
"Look, I did not forget
to come to the party," said Deb.

Lots of caps

A man had ten caps for sale.
He put all the caps on top
of his head.
"Caps for sale. Caps for sale,"
he said.
"Big caps. Little caps.
Caps for sale."
No one came to get a cap.

The man sat down by a tree.

He was hot, so hot.

He went to sleep.

Zzzzzzz. Zzzzzzz. Zzzzzzz.

When he woke up
he had one cap on his head,
but that was all.
He looked and looked
for his caps.

"Ttt. Ttt. Ttt. Ttt."

The man looked up.

Lots of monkeys sat in the tree.

"Give me my caps," said the man.

"Ttt. Ttt," said the monkeys and
they clapped their hands.

"Give me my caps,"
said the man and
he stamped his feet.
"Ttt. Ttt," said the monkeys and
they stamped their feet.

The man was cross.
He took off his cap and
threw it down.
The monkeys took off their
caps and threw them down.

So the man put on his cap.

He put all the caps on to his head.

"Caps for sale.

Caps for sale," he said.

He went down the road.

"Big caps. Little caps.

Caps for sale."

"Ttt. Ttt," said the monkeys

in the tree.

"Ttt. Ttt. Ttt. Ttt."